Disney Junior

BIG BOOK OF FUN

PaRragon

Bath · New York · Cologne · Melbourne · Delhi
Hong Kong · Shenzhen · Singapore · Amsterdam

This edition published by Parragon Books Ltd in 2015

Parragon Books Ltd
Chartist House
15–17 Trim Street
Bath BA1 1HA, UK
www.parragon.com

Copyright © 2015 Disney Enterprises, Inc.

All rights reserved. No part of this publication may be reproduced, stored in a retrieval system or transmitted, in any form or by any means, electronic, mechanical, photocopying, recording or otherwise, without the prior permission of the copyright holder.

ISBN 978-1-4748-0303-8

Printed in China

Disney Junior

BIG BOOK OF FUN

Contents

MICKEY MOUSE CLUBHOUSE

UP, UP AND AWAY!

By **Sheila Sweeny Higginson**
Illustrated by the **Disney Storybook Artists**
Designed by **Elizabeth Andaluz**

Donald and his friends were standing outside the Clubhouse on a crisp, bright day.

"Oh, Donald," Daisy said, "look at the sky! It's lovely!"

"Shhh!" Donald whispered. "Don't make a move! Something is following me and I'm going to find out who – or what – it is!"

Daisy giggled as she looked behind Donald. "Oh, my!" she said. "There *is* something following you! It's wearing a sailor's cap – just like yours. It's got cute webbed feet – just like yours. And when you move, it moves, too."

"Aw, phooey," Donald quacked as he turned round and saw ... his shadow! "That is a fine-looking shape, but I still don't trust it!"

Donald glared at his shadow.

"Cheer up, buddy," Mickey said. "Why don't you leave your shadow on the ground and come with me?"

"I don't know," Donald said, moping. "Where are we going?"

"Up, up and away!" Mickey cheered. "Who wants to help Minnie and me fly our hot-air balloon?"

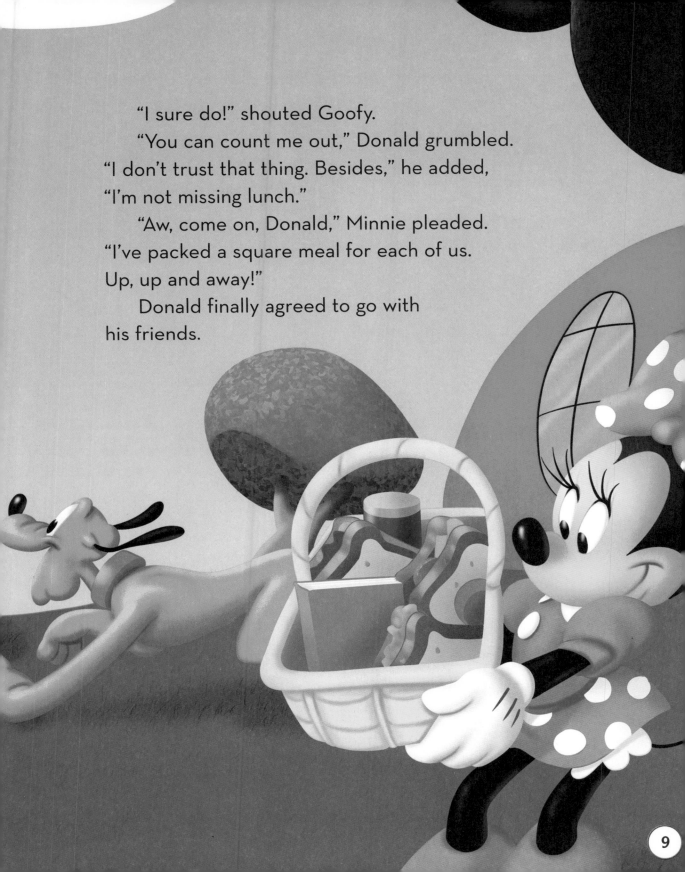

"I sure do!" shouted Goofy.

"You can count me out," Donald grumbled. "I don't trust that thing. Besides," he added, "I'm not missing lunch."

"Aw, come on, Donald," Minnie pleaded. "I've packed a square meal for each of us. Up, up and away!"

Donald finally agreed to go with his friends.

"Something's wrong," Mickey said. "The balloon won't fill with air!"

"That's too bad, buddy," said Donald, trying to hide a grin. "I guess we'll just have to go back to the Clubhouse for lunch."

"Oh, Toodles!" Mickey said. "Do we have a Mousketool that can help?" Toodles appeared. "Do any of you know how we can use this?" Mickey asked his friends.

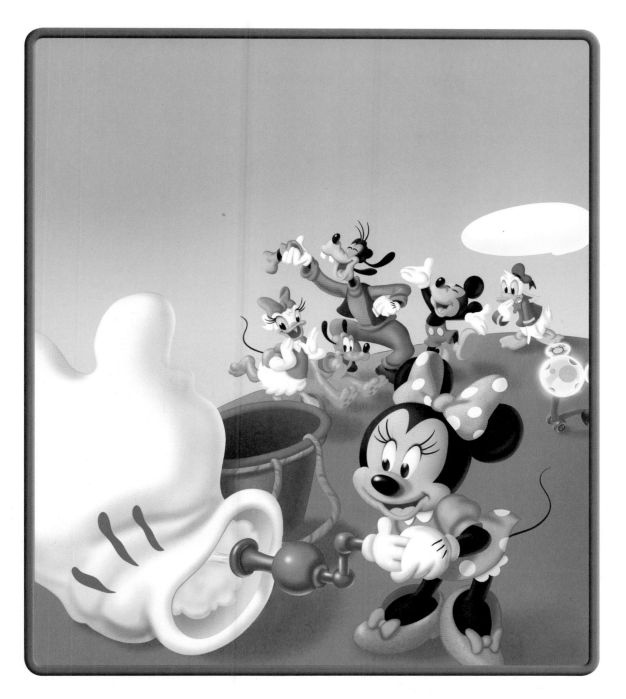

"I know, Mickey!" answered Minnie. "We can turn the handle to inflate the balloon with hot air."

"Why, you're right, Minnie!" Mickey shouted. "We've got ears! Say cheers!"

Soon, the friends were floating high in the sky.
"Up, up and away!" cried Daisy. "This is fun!"
"Look, everyone!" yelled Minnie. "Can you see the
Clubhouse from here? It looks so small! And there are
so many shapes below us. I see a heart and a rectangle.
What do you see?"

"I see a triangle!" Mickey said. "And there are Chip and Dale playing a round of golf!"

"It should be called a triangle of golf," laughed Daisy. "Just look at all those triangle-shaped flags!"

"What's a triangle?" asked Goofy, as he bit into his sandwich.

"A triangle is a shape with three sides that all have points at the ends – sort of like your sandwich," Minnie explained.

"Or like that?" Goofy questioned, as he pointed to a huge triangle in front of the balloon. It was the top of a mountain!

Suddenly, a gust of wind whisked the friends right towards it!

"We need help," cried Mickey. "Oh, Toodles!"

Toodles appeared with a triangle, a patch, a ladder and a spyglass.

"Which tool should we use?" asked Minnie.

"Let's try them all!" said Mickey. "Daisy, ring the triangle for help!" Daisy rang the triangle, but it didn't help them get off the mountain.

"Minnie, patch the hole!" cried Mickey. Minnie put a square patch on the round hole in the balloon, but it was too small.

"Goofy, look through the spyglass!" shouted Mickey. Goofy held the spyglass and saw that the ground looked very far away.

"There's only one tool left," yelled Mickey. "To the ladder!"

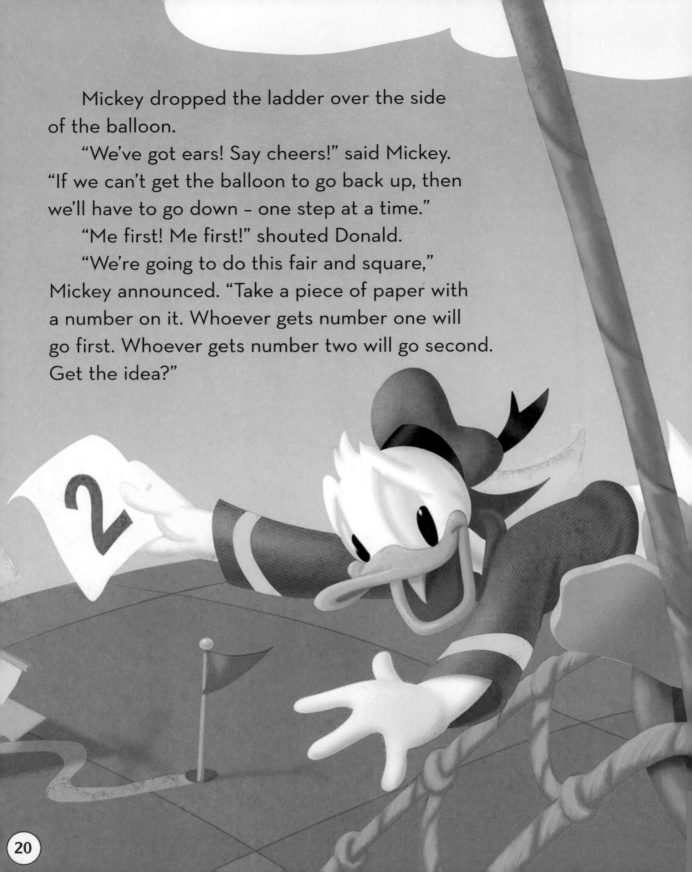

Mickey dropped the ladder over the side of the balloon.

"We've got ears! Say cheers!" said Mickey. "If we can't get the balloon to go back up, then we'll have to go down – one step at a time."

"Me first! Me first!" shouted Donald.

"We're going to do this fair and square," Mickey announced. "Take a piece of paper with a number on it. Whoever gets number one will go first. Whoever gets number two will go second. Get the idea?"

The friends climbed down the ladder one by one.
Everyone was happy to be standing on firm ground again.
"We're in great shape, unlike our balloon," said
Mickey. "But we're going to have to hike back home.
It's not far – just down that path ... or maybe it's that
other one...."

The friends trudged along, growing more and more tired.
"I think we've been walking in circles," Mickey finally said.
"I'm sure I've seen this tree before."

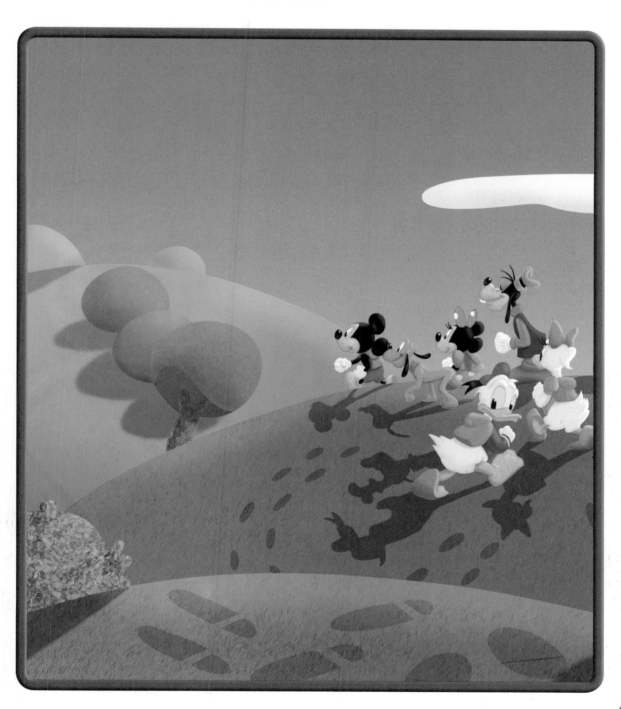

The friends needed help to get back to the Clubhouse. "Oh, Toodles!" Mickey called.

Toodles appeared, showing three pictures of Mickey.

Mickey shared them with his friends: "I'm standing in front of the Clubhouse and my shadow is different in each picture. In the morning, my shadow falls in front of me. At noon, I have no shadow. In the evening, my shadow falls behind me. Do any of you know what this could mean?"

"I've got it!" Donald shouted. "Right now, it's late and the Sun is setting behind us. Toodles shows that in the evening, our shadows point towards the Clubhouse. If we follow them, they'll lead us back home."

Donald was right! The shadows helped the friends walk in the right direction. Soon, they arrived back at the Clubhouse. Everyone was hungry from the long trip.

"Well, Donald," Daisy said, "do you trust your shadow now?"

"I'll trust the handsome guy to lead me home," Donald answered. "But he better not ask me to share my sandwich!"

The End

Bubble Trouble

Based on an episode written by Kent Redeker
Based on the series created by Chris Nee
Adapted by Sheila Sweeny Higginson
Illustrated by Alan Batson

Doc likes to play with her best friend Emmie and her little sister Alma.

One of their favourite toys is a Bubble Monkey bubble blower.

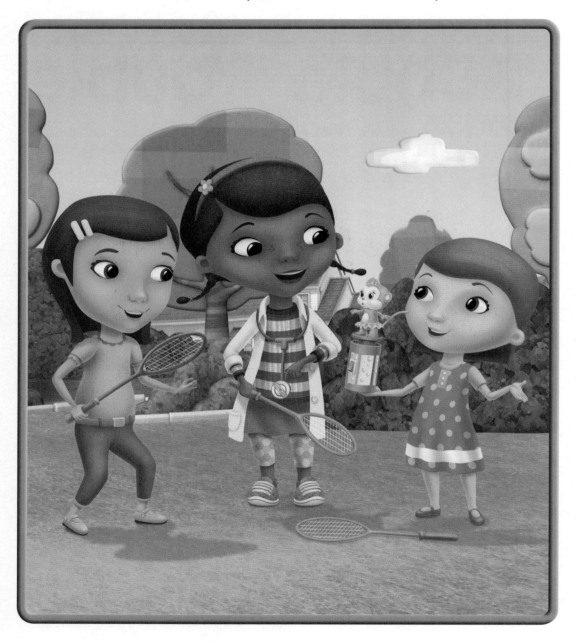

Emmie puts Bubble Monkey on the picnic
table and flips her switch. One, two, three ...

... bubbles, bubbles everywhere!
Alma pops three bubbles and Emmie
pops six. Doc pops two bubbles at once!

Emmie's dog Rudi wants to pop bubbles, too.
But Bubble Monkey soon stops working.
She's all out of bubbles.

Alma fills up Bubble Monkey while Doc and Emmie
chase after Rudi. She asks, "Is everyone ready?"
They are!

One, two, three –
but no bubbles!

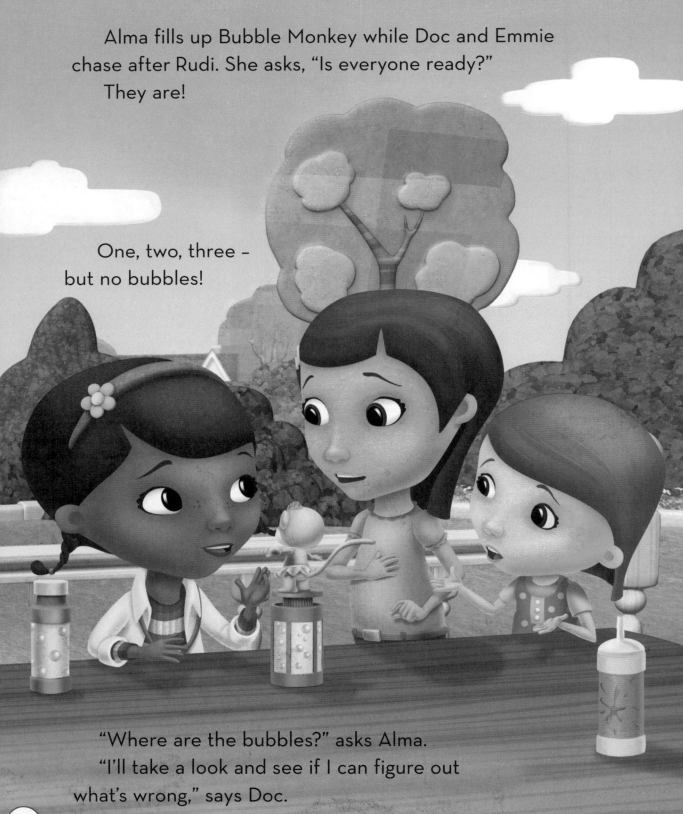

"Where are the bubbles?" asks Alma.
"I'll take a look and see if I can figure out
what's wrong," says Doc.

Doc takes Bubble Monkey to her clinic and brings her to life with her magic stethoscope.

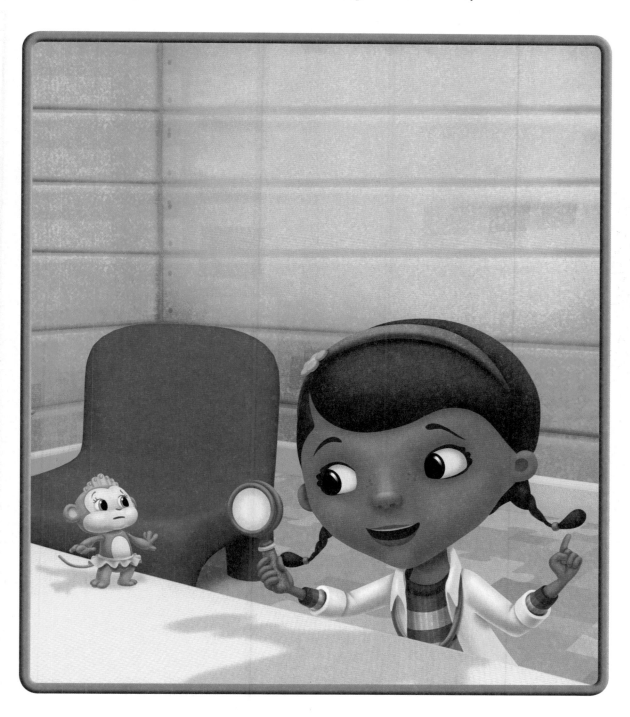

First, Doc runs some tests and takes a feather from her bag. She asks Bubble Monkey to blow the feather. Bubble Monkey blows, but it barely moves.

Next, Doc listens to Bubble Monkey's chest.

"Sounds like goop is blocking your bubble pumper," she says. "Are you having any other symptoms?"

"Well, I have a tummy ache," Bubble Monkey says.

"Can I give your tummy a little squeeze?" Doc asks.

She presses Bubble Monkey's tummy. Something shoots out and hits Stuffy in the chest.

"Ick!" says Stuffy.

Now Stuffy and Chilly are stuck together!
"Weird," says Doc as she pulls them apart. "This is glue."

Doc heads back to Emmie's garden to investigate.
"Alma, what did you put in Bubble Monkey?" she asks.

Alma holds up the pink jar. "I used this," she says. "Alma, the pink one is glue!" Emmie says. "The green one is the bubble soap!"

Doc rushes back to the clinic.
"I have a diagnosis!" she tells Bubble Monkey. "You have
a bad case of Gunk-inside-atude."

"Toys need to get filled properly, just like people need to eat right," says Doc.

Then Doc cleans out Bubble Monkey's tubes and fills her up with bubble soap.

"Thanks, Doc. I feel better! You're super-fantastic!"
Bubble Monkey says, cheering.

"I love my job!" says Doc. "Now let's get you back
to Emmie and Alma."

"I'm back!" Doc says. "And this time, I brought Bubble Monkey!"

"Did you fix her?" Alma asks.

"There's only one way to find out," says Doc.

One ... two ... three ...

Bubbles!

The End

46

MICKEY MOUSE CLUBHOUSE

FUN ACTIVITIES!

Hi, there! Do you want to come to my Clubhouse?

Just colour me in and say, "Meeska, Mooska, Mickey Mouse!"

Here it is – the Clubhouse! Colour it in and come on inside!

Colour this picture of the kitchen. It has an oven, a sink and a ... leaping frog! Hey, what's he doing here?

Can you help Pluto find the frog in this picture?
Then colour in the picture.

Answer:

Daisy has found the frog!
Colour this picture of the frog in her basket.

Match the leaping frog to its shadow.

Answer:

Come on back to the Clubhouse. It looks like Daisy needs help getting ready for a surprise party! Colour this picture.

Daisy and Mickey blew up all these balloons!
Find two that are exactly the same and colour them in.

Answer:

Daisy is baking a cake. How many eggs is she using?
Circle the number.

1 2 3 4 5 6 7 8 9 10

Answer: 2

The cake is finished! You can help to decorate it.
Draw four candles on top of the cake.

'Pin the Tail on the Donkey' is Goofy's favourite party game.
He is trying to put the tail in the right place.

Now it's your turn! Draw a tail on this donkey.

It's getting late and the guests are leaving the party. Oh, Toodles!
Which of these objects will help them to find their way in the dark?
Point to the correct object.

Answer:

The torch.

Who has Donald found hiding on the path?

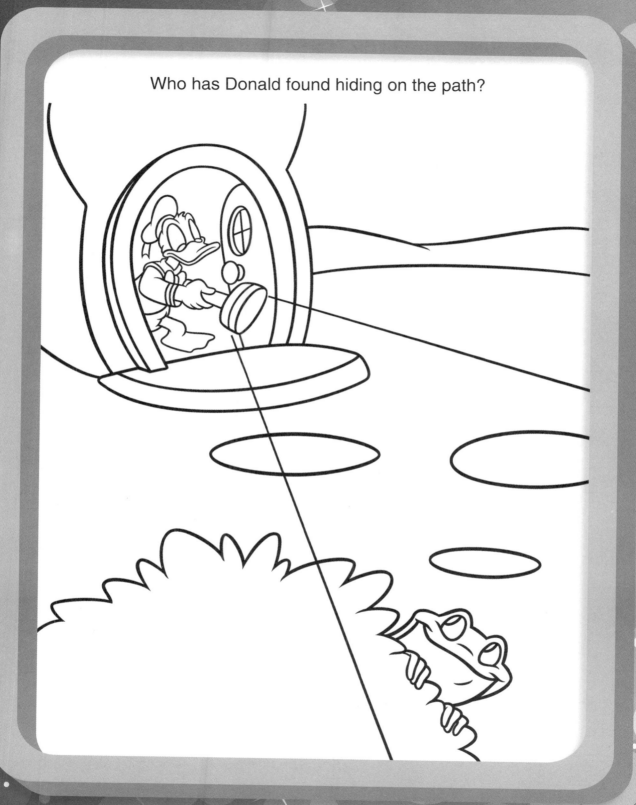

It's time for an out-of-this-world adventure! Colour this picture of Goofy blasting off to outer space! Go, Goofy!

Help Goofy get to Mars – draw a path for his spaceship to follow.

Answer:

How many planets are in Goofy's path?
Circle the number, then colour in the picture.

1 2 3 4 5 6 7 8 9 10

Answer:

4

Three of these spaceships look the same.
Goofy's spaceship is different. Can you find Goofy's ship?

Answer:

Goofy needs help getting down from his spaceship.
Which Mouseketool should he use? Point to the correct object.

Answer:

The slide.

Goofy has invited four aliens back to the Clubhouse!
Colour this picture of Goofy and his new friends.

Draw a line to match each alien to its shadow.

Answers:

Welcome to the Clubhouse garden! Colour this picture
of Minnie and Daisy doing some gardening.

Minnie has taken some photographs in the garden.
How many pictures are there? Circle the number.

1 2 3 4 5 6 7 8 9 10

Answer:

Minnie is picking some flowers to make a bunch.
Help her by colouring in the flowers.

Colour in this picture of Daisy wearing a flower chain!

Can you find one tree, two sunflowers, three birds, four bees and five friends in this picture? Circle them as you find them.

Answers:

Draw a line to match each picture with the correct number.

1

2

3

4

5

Answers:

We're having a great day at the zoo! Write how many legs each animal has on the ground.

Write the numbers one to five to put these zoo animals
in size order, from smallest to biggest.

_____

_____

_____

_____

_____

Answer:

The seal pond is Pluto's favourite place at the zoo.
The seals are throwing a ball.

The monkeys are swinging from the branches.

Draw a line to match each animal to its shadow.

Answers:

Help Goofy through the maze to find his way to the penguins.

Answer:

What a great day! Now I want to read a book.
Colour in Mickey's story time.

It's bedtime! That means it's time for me to put my book away.

TREASURE HUNT
ACTIVITIES!

Join Jake's pirate crew – draw yourself as a pirate.

Remember to add these pirate items.

spyglass	eye patch
compass	sword
coin purse	pirate hat

Now that you're part of the pirate crew,
it's time to go to Pirate Island!
Which line on the map leads there?
Remember: 'X' marks the spot!

Answer: Line 2

Every pirate crew needs ... a hideout!
Look at these two pictures of the hideout.
Find and circle five differences.

Colour in a skull and crossbones every time you find a difference.

Answers:

You're up in the hideout's crow's nest with Jake.
Which of these ships is the Jolly Roger? Circle it and say,
"The Jolly Roger be heading this way!"

Answer:

How many times can you find the word PIRATE in this wordsearch? Circle the words as you find them.

X	M	Y	N	O	P	E	P
P	P	I	R	A	T	E	I
I	O	I	B	A	I	I	R
R	U	X	R	R	W	R	A
A	R	U	T	A	O	Q	T
T	P	P	I	R	A	T	E
E	E	E	R	A	K	L	Y
P	I	R	A	T	E	I	N

Answer:

5

Yo-ho, way to go!
Colour in Jake, Izzy, Cubby and Skully.

Draw a line to match the pirates to their property.

Answers:

All shipshape and seaworthy pirates have their own skull and crossbones.

This is Jake's:

This is Captain Hook's:

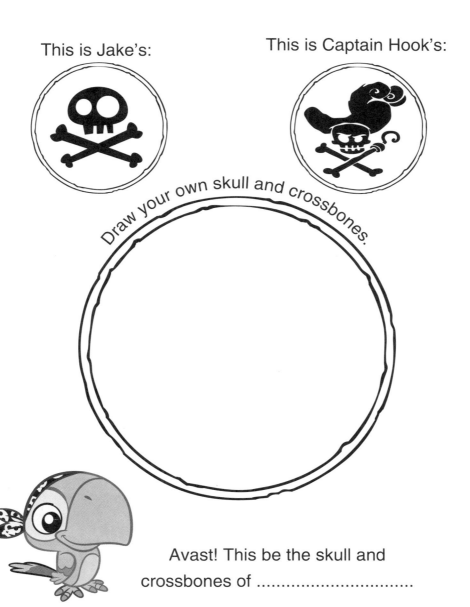

Draw your own skull and crossbones.

Avast! This be the skull and crossbones of ....

Shiver me timbers! Captain Hook is spying on
Jake and his pirate crew. Colour in the pesky pirate.

Jake has noticed that something odd has washed up on the beach.... Look at the two pictures below – can you spy the difference?

Answer:

Jake and his crew want to return Hook's hat
to him because it's the right thing to do.
Can you guide Bucky and the pirate crew
through the maze to the Jolly Roger?

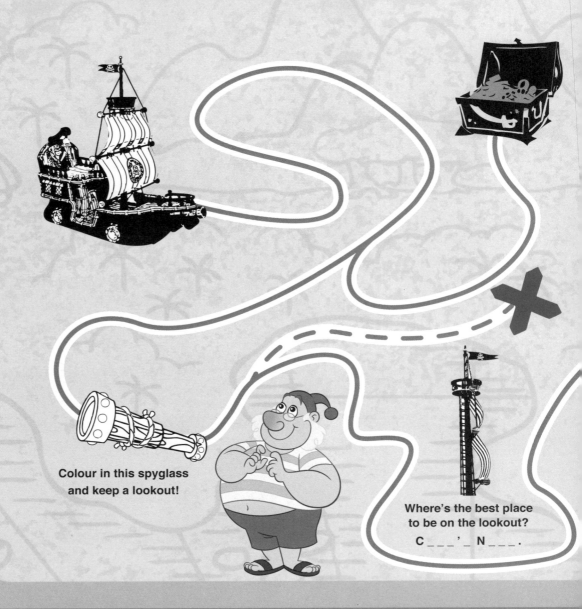

Colour in this spyglass
and keep a lookout!

Where's the best place
to be on the lookout?
C _ _ _ ' _ N _ _ _ .

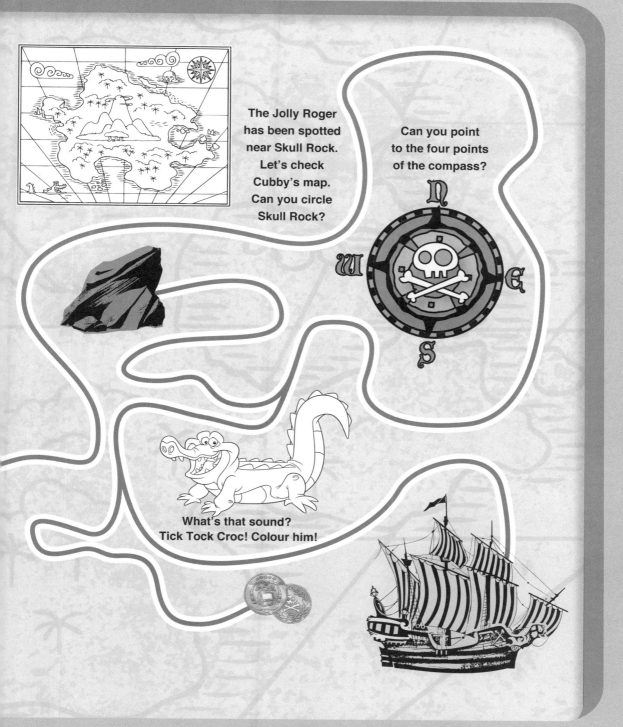

The Jolly Roger has been spotted near Skull Rock. Let's check Cubby's map. Can you circle Skull Rock?

Can you point to the four points of the compass?

What's that sound? Tick Tock Croc! Colour him!

Answer:

Help Jake climb up the rope net to get aboard the Jolly Roger.
Use the key to move through the maze.

Key:

Move Left

Move Up

Finish

Start

Answer:

Hook is happy to have his hat back, but he wishes those scallywags hadn't had so much fun returning it! Join the dots and colour in Captain Hook's hat.

It's Skully's birthday and Jake, Izzy and Cubby
are throwing him a party.
Draw a present for Skully below.

Skully's joke corner:
Q: What do pirates ask when
someone leaves a door open?
A: Were you born in a barn-acle?

Look at the picture of Skully's party
and answer the questions below.

1. How many party hats can you count? _____

2. Circle the correct sentence.

Jake is wearing a headscarf.   Jake is wearing a neckscarf.

3. Who has a bag of pixie dust around her neck? _____

4. Jake, Izzy and Cubby are children. Skully is a _____ .

Write your own pirate adventure
and draw pictures to match in
these boxes. The first story box
has been done for you.

1. It's Skully's birthday. Jake and
the crew have planned a party.
But, oh, no! Captain Hook has
stolen all Skully's presents!

Hints and tips:
● Make sure your story has
a beginning, a middle and an end.
● Who are the characters in your story?
● Where is the story taking place?
● What is happening in your story?

Remember: there's no limit to your
imagination, so get creative!

2.

3.

Skully's joke corner:
Q: How much does a pirate pay for a peg leg and a hook?
A: An arm and a leg!
ROLF   LOL
LOL   ROFL   LOL
Ha ha

4. _____
_____
_____

6. _____
_____
_____

5. _____
_____
_____

Take it in turns with a friend to connect two of the dots with a line. If your line completes a square, put your initial in it. Continue until all the dots are joined up. The player with the most boxes is the winner!

Grab a piratey friend and decide which of you is going to be Jake and which of you is going to be Hook. Take it in turns to draw either a sword (for Jake) or a hook (for Hook). The first player to get three in a row is the winner!

Captain Hook and Mr Smee have taken Skully's presents to Shipwreck Rock. How will Jake and the crew get them back?

Cross out every 'A' to discover the answer and copy the remaining letters on to the lines below.

AFAALAY WAAIATAH IAAZAZAAYAAS PAIAAXAIAE ADUASAAT

_ _ _   _ _ _ _   _ _ _ _ _   ,

_ _ _ _ _   _ _ _ .

Skully's joke corner:
Q: Why did the pirate cross the sea?
A: To get to the other tide!
ROLF LOL Ha ha LOL ROFL Ha ha LOL

Answer: FLY WITH IZZY'S PIXIE DUST.

Hooray! The pirate crew can finally have a party for Skully!
Complete the scene by giving everyone a party hat,
then colour them in!

Jake's sword was given to him by Peter Pan so he could be a good leader. Are you a good leader, too? Draw your pirate sword below.

Oh, no! That sneaky snook Captain Hook has stolen Jake's sword. Can you find it below?

Answer:

Jake and the crew are chasing Captain Hook and
Mr Smee because they've stolen Jake's sword. Guide Jake
through the maze to get his sword back.

Answer:

Jake and the pirate crew have followed Captain Hook
to a canyon, but Hook has pushed the log bridge into
the canyon, so they can't cross. Izzy has a plan ...
they can use her pixie dust to fly over!

1. Which of these pictures shows Izzy using her pixie dust? _____

1.
2.
3.
4.

Read these sentences. Are they true or false? Circle the answer.

2. Izzy is in every picture.

   true   false

3. Skully is flying in all the pictures.

   true   false

Answers:
3 – false.
2 – true;
1 – 3;

Hook is trying to open a mysterious door using Jake's sword as a key. Which shape will Jake's sword fit into?

1.

2.

3.

4.

Answer:

4

In each section, circle your favourite and find out which pirate you are most like.

1. Possession

a. sword

b. map

c. pixie dust

d. Captain Hook's hat

2. Hobby

a. sailing

b. playing harmonica

c. flying

d. napping

3. Catchphrase

a. "Yo-ho! Let's go!"

b. "Aw, coconuts!"

c. "Shiver me timbers!"

d. "I never have any fun!"

Mostly a
You're most like Jake. You're the leader of the crew and always include your best friends in the fun.

Mostly c
You're most like Izzy. You are full of ideas and you always think things through carefully.

Mostly b
You're most like Cubby. You're always rarin' to go-go-GO! You always overcome your fears and act bravely.

Mostly d
Oh dear, you're most like Captain Hook. You're a sneaky snook, who doesn't like to see other people have fun.

At the door, the crew find a message from Peter Pan:
"Only a great leader can open this door,
with an enchanted sword and nothing more."
Look at the clues and write the answers in the grid.
The name of the person who can open the door will
appear in the shaded boxes.

1. __ __ __ __ __ Roger.

2. __ __ __ .

3. __ __ __ __ __ .

4. Crow's __ __ __ __ .

4 – Nest. The great leader is Jake.
Answer: 1 – Jolly; 2 – Map; 3 – Rock;

The Never Land pirates are dancing to a rocking sea shanty.
Colour them in.

Make your own pirate song by circling
the words at the end of each verse that
you like the most.

On the shores of Never Land,
There's a pirate crew   *you know!*   *yo-ho!*

For new adventures, they set sail,
Yo-ho!   *Let's go!*   *Let's row!*

Hook, he wants to spoil the fun,
Hear him cry,   *"Avast!"*   *"The last!"*

Jake's pirate crew have fun in the sun,
Every day is such   *a blast!*   *a laugh!*

Colour in your favourite instrument below,
then draw yourself in a pirate band with Cubby.

Captain Hook is not happy with the scallywags
who are making that rat-a-tat racket.
Colour him in or walk the plank!

Hook has spotted who is making the noise through his spyglass.
How many music notes can you count?

Answer:

02

Oh, no! Captain Hook and Mr Smee have stolen Cubby's drums. Help Jake and the pirate crew follow the musical notes to the sneaky pirates.

Answer:

These two pirates love to burst into song at the drop of a gang plank. Circle five differences between the two pictures.

Answers:

Join the dots to complete the picture of Never Land.

Draw a line and match each pirate to their shadow.

1

2

3

4

5

6

A

B

C

D

E

F

Complete this dot-to-dot of Bucky and colour it in.

Look at this picture of Captain Hook and Smee.
Find and circle six differences between the two pictures.
Hint: There is one difference in each grid square.

What are Jake and Skully saying?
Can you trace over the letters to find out?

"Crackers!"

"Ahoy, mateys!"

ACTIVITY ADVENTURES!

Ellyvan has come to play football. Oh dear, no one else is here!
Colour this picture of Ellyvan and the empty pitch.

Taxicrab is making smoothies for his friends. They have just finished a game of football. But where was Ellyvan?

Find the path that leads to the goal.

Answer:

Oh, dear! Ellyvan missed the game. Colour him in.

Colour this picture of Bungo telling Ellyvan about
the goal he scored to win the game.

Tomorrow is the day for the big Coconut Run Road Race.
"Don't be late, Ellyvan!" says Taxicrab.

Can you help Bungo and Dozer fill the holes in the road?
Draw lines to connect the right shapes to the right holes.

Answers:

Zoom! The Coconut Run Road Race is underway!

Toadhog and Zooter are nearly at the finish line!

Zooter wins! Join the dots to complete the picture.

1

2

3

4

5

6

7

8

9

10

11

12

13

Colour this picture of Zooter receiving the trophy!
Hooray for Zooter!

Miss Jolly and the Beetlebugs are going to check
on Ellyvan. He missed the race!

How many Beetlebugs can you count?
Write your answer in the circle.

Answer:

8

"I went to the starting line but no one else was there," says Ellyvan. "So I came home."

"You were too early!" says Miss Jolly. "The race was in the afternoon, not the morning."

Bungo has made signs to help Ellyvan learn the parts of the day.
Help Ellyvan by numbering the signs in this order –
1. Morning, 2. Afternoon, 3. Night.

Answer:

Morning is when Ellyvan eats his breakfast of cereal and fruit.

"Afternoon starts with lunchtime and goes all the way to suppertime," says Bungo.

Can you match these friends to their shadows?

Answers:

"The picnic is tomorrow afternoon, Ellyvan,"
says Hippobus. "Don't forget!"

The next day, Ellyvan is on time for the picnic!
But where is everyone else?

Eight of Ellyvan's friends are hiding in this picture.
Can you find them?

Answer:

Colour this picture of everyone jumping out to surprise Ellyvan. "You're right on time!" they shout.

"Hooray!" says Ellyvan. "I was hungry!" What a wonderful picnic!

Toadhog is up on the roof fixing his weathervane.

The Beetlebugs are going on a field trip.
Careful! There's a bumpy road ahead!

Which picture of Miss Jolly is different to the others?

A.

B.

C.

D.

Answer:

B

Can you help Miss Jolly find the way to Toadhog's house? The road signs will help you.

Whoops! Toadhog slips. He is falling into the river!

"We've come to learn about your wonderful water wheel!" says Miss Jolly to Toadhog.

"Flowing river water turns the water wheel," Toadhog explains. "That makes power for the whole town."

This is Bobby! How many pictures of
him can you find in the grid below?

Answer:

4

Colour this picture of Toadhog and the
Beetlebugs having a group photograph taken.
Smile, everyone!

Oh dear, Toadhog is frowning in the photograph!

"We have to cheer up Toadhog!" Mrs Jolly tells the Beetlebugs.

Maybe this will make Toadhog smile!

Whee!

Find and circle three flowers
and five pineapples on this page.

Answer:

The Royal
Slumber Party

Written by Catherine Hapka • Based on an episode by Erica Rothschild
Illustrated by Character Building Studio and the Disney Storybook Artists

Sofia and Amber are having a royal sleepover tonight!
"This is where we'll be sleeping," Amber says.
"The observatory? We'll sleep under the stars!" Sofia cries.
"It's a royal slumber party," Amber says. "Everything has to be amazing."

The royal herald's trumpet sounds.

"Our friends are here!" Sofia cries.

Amber's two friends, Princess Hildegard and Princess Clio, step out of their coaches. Behind them are Jade and Ruby in an oxcart.

"I can't believe we're here!" Jade exclaims, hugging Sofia.

"We're so excited!" Ruby adds.

Once everyone has put on their nightgowns,
Ruby and Jade twist their hair with pine cone rollers.
The other princesses stare at them.
"What are they wearing?" Hildegard says.
"What are they doing?" Clio wonders.
Amber frowns. "Are those pine cones?"
Ruby hears her and dances over. "Do you want one?
We brought extras."

Amber marches over to Sofia. "Sofia! Pine cones are
not part of a perfect princess slumber party."

Sofia is worried. She wants her new sister and her
old friends to like each other.

"They can fit in, Amber," she says. "They just need
a little help."

Sofia has a great idea. "How would you two like a royal makeover?" she asks her friends.

Ruby and Jade squeal with excitement!

Baileywick and Sofia's woodland friends help out. They fix the girls' hair and dress them in pretty gowns and sparkling tiaras.

Sofia makes her friends cover their eyes. Then she leads them to a mirror. "Open your eyes," she says.

Jade and Ruby gasp when they see themselves.

"I'm a princess!" Ruby exclaims.

"Me, too!" cries Jade.

Now it's time for party activities.
First comes fan decorating.
Ruby and Jade have fun, but their
fans don't look very princessy.

Next the girls play a game of Pin the Tail
on the Unicorn.
"Ooh! Ooh!" Jade says. "Can I go first?"
But Jade ends up nowhere
near the unicorn!

Then the girls watch Cedric, the royal sorcerer, put on a magic puppet show in the banquet hall. During the show, James, Sofia's brother, walks in with a message for the girls.

"Prince James!" Jade and Ruby cry, rushing towards him. They're thrilled to see the friendly prince!

Jade and Ruby are so excited that they accidentally knock over the chocolate-milk fountain. Oops!

Chocolate milk splashes on to Amber's nightgown. She is furious!

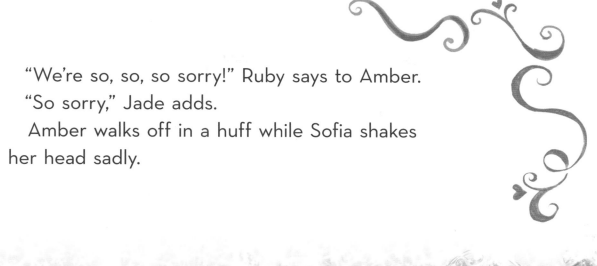

"We're so, so, so sorry!" Ruby says to Amber.
"So sorry," Jade adds.

Amber walks off in a huff while Sofia shakes
her head sadly.

Baileywick hurries Jade and Ruby away to get cleaned up. Then James tells the girls it's time for some dancing in the throne room.

"Let's go," Amber says. "Maybe we can enjoy five minutes of our party without Sofia's friends making a mess."

Now Sofia is even more worried! She goes to find her friends.

"I just want you both to fit in with the princesses," Sofia explains.

"We look just like them now, don't we?" Jade asks.

"Yes," Sofia says. "But princesses don't talk as much, or laugh as loud, or make as much mess."

Jade frowns. "We were just having fun."

"We're sorry," Ruby adds quickly. "We'll try to act more like Amber and the other princesses."

"Thank you!" Sofia is relieved. Now she's sure everyone will get along!

Sofia and her friends join the others in the throne room. But Ruby and Jade don't know how to waltz. All they can do is stand there and watch the four princesses dance.

After a while, they tell Sofia that they would like to go home.

"But you're finally fitting in!" Sofia cries. "And you're not embarrassing me!"

"I'm sorry if we talk too much and laugh too loudly for your fancy new friends," says Jade. "Maybe we shouldn't be friends any more!"

Ruby takes Jade's arm and together they rush out of the room.

"Don't worry about them," Hildegard tells Sofia. "You're with us now."

179

Sofia goes after her friends but finds her mother instead.
"I was trying to help Jade and Ruby fit in," she explains.
"But I made them feel bad."

"A true princess treats people with kindness, Sofia,"
Queen Miranda says gently. "If someone is your friend,
you should like them for who they are."

180

Sofia knows her mother is right. She runs outside
and finds her friends as they are about to leave.

"I'm sorry about the way I acted," she says. "Please let
me make it up to you. We can have our own slumber
party – just the three of us!"

Jade and Ruby think for a moment and then finally
agree to stay.

Soon Sofia and her friends are in her room having a great time. They laugh - loudly! They talk - a lot! They roll pine cones in their hair and put tiaras on top.

Meanwhile, Amber and her friends go back to the observatory.
"Finally, it's just us princesses," Amber says.
"This is a perfect party," Hildegard agrees with a yawn.
There's a long silence. The princesses are really bored.
"You know," Clio says, "Sofia's friends were kind of fun."

A moment later, Amber and her friends knock on Sofia's door.

"Um, do you have room for a few more princesses?" asks Amber.

Sofia looks at Jade and Ruby. "What do you think?"

"The more, the merrier," Ruby says with a smile.

Sofia and Amber end up having the perfect sleepover with friends – old and new!

The End

FOLLOW THAT SOUND!

WRITTEN BY MELINDA LA ROSE

ILLUSTRATED BY ALAN BATSON

One day on Shipwreck Beach, Cubby is playing his harmonica.

"Aw, coconuts! I'll never be ready in time to play at Marina's party," says Cubby sadly.

Hook is drifting off to sleep in his hammock, when suddenly he is startled awake by the sound of music! "One of those puny pirates is making an awful racket with his blowy music thing!" says Hook.

"Why don't you ask the sea pups nicely if they'll be a little quieter?" says Smee.

"Smee, who do you think you're dealing with?" says Hook. "Why would I ask nicely when I can take the blowy thing away!"

Hook uses his fishing hook to nab the harmonica right out of Cubby's mouth!

Swoosh!

"My harmonica!" says Cubby.
"We gotta get it back!" says Jake.

Smee blows into the harmonica. It makes a terrible noise!

Weeeeee-yooouuu!

Startled, Smee throws the harmonica up in the air ...
but it doesn't come back down!

"Um, Cap'n," says Smee, "the
harmonica just disappeared!"

"Crackers!" says Skully. "That monkey took the harmonica!"

"He's heading for the Never Jungle," says Cubby.

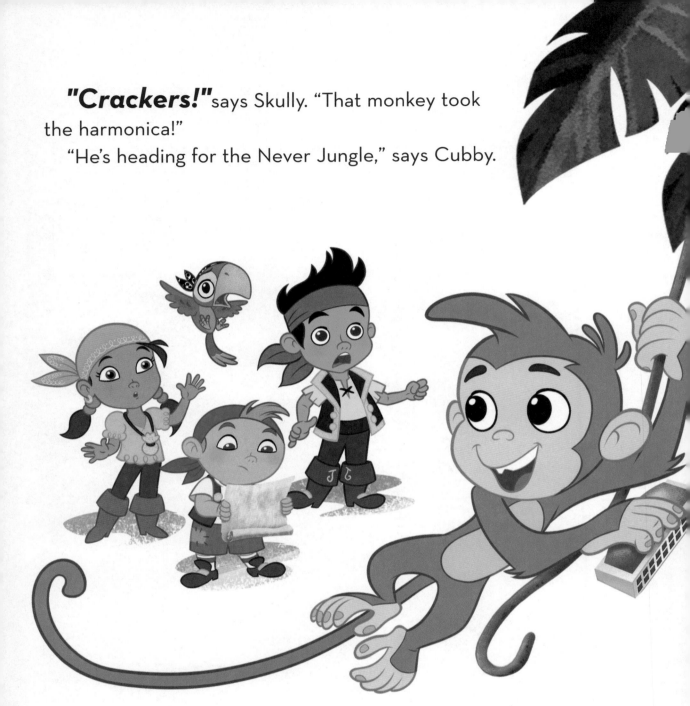

"Come on, crew," says Jake. "Follow that monkey!"

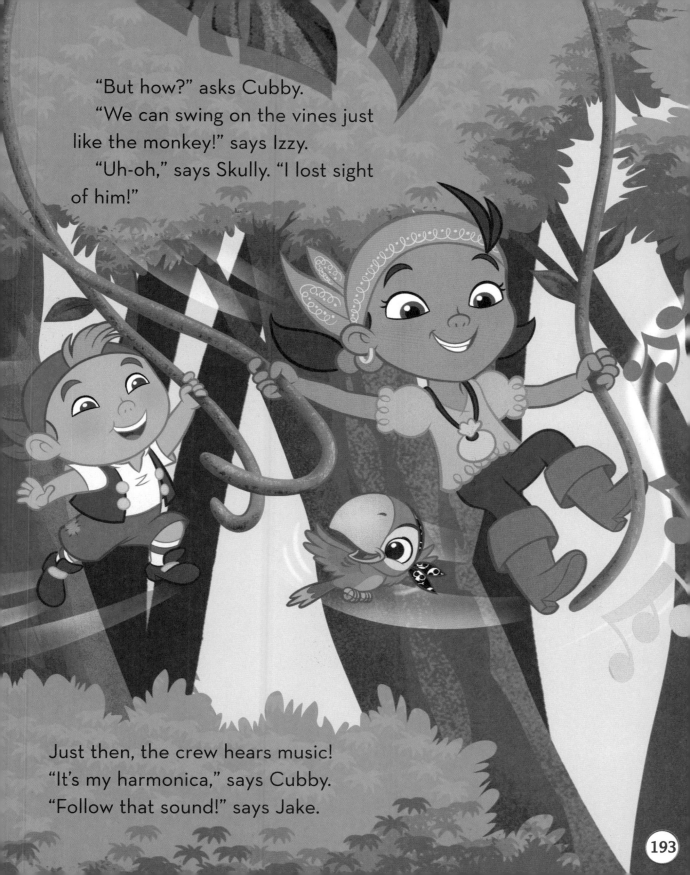

"But how?" asks Cubby.

"We can swing on the vines just like the monkey!" says Izzy.

"Uh-oh," says Skully. "I lost sight of him!"

Just then, the crew hears music!

"It's my harmonica," says Cubby.

"Follow that sound!" says Jake.

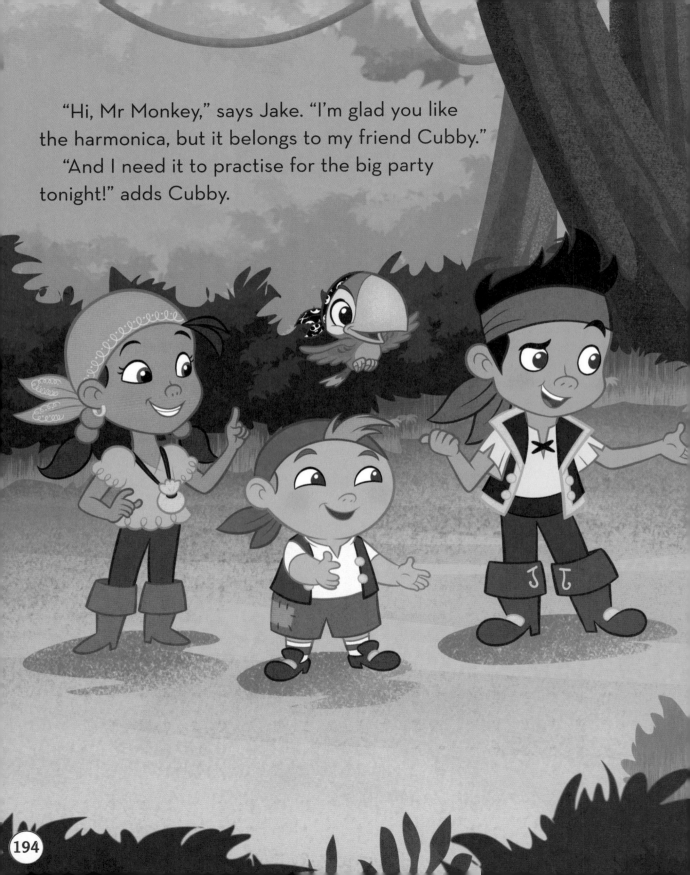

"Hi, Mr Monkey," says Jake. "I'm glad you like the harmonica, but it belongs to my friend Cubby."

"And I need it to practise for the big party tonight!" adds Cubby.

"He doesn't want to give the harmonica back," says Izzy.

"If only we had another instrument," says Jake. "Then we could trade with the monkey."

"That's a great idea," says Izzy.

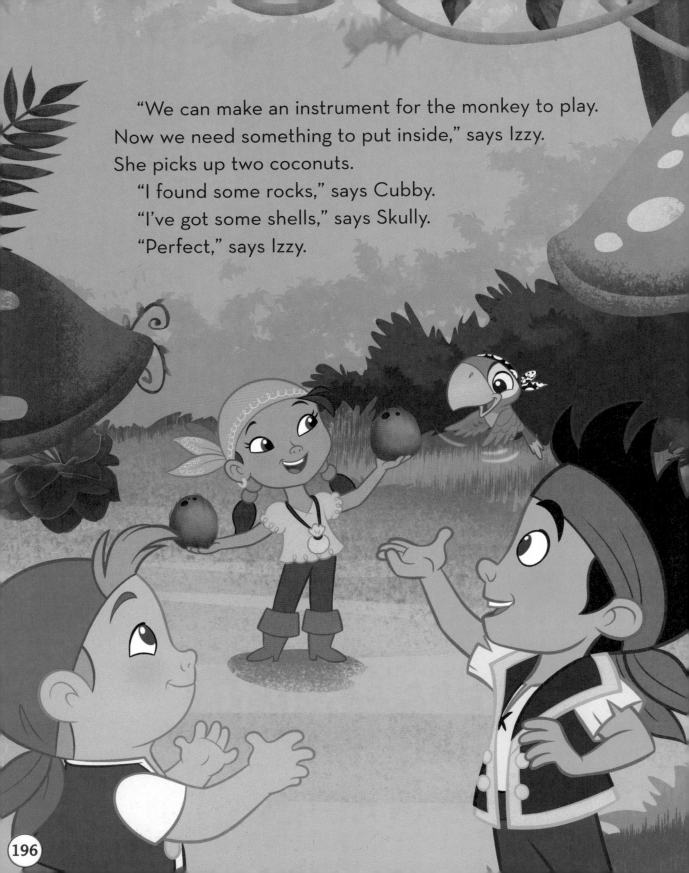

"We can make an instrument for the monkey to play.
Now we need something to put inside," says Izzy.
She picks up two coconuts.
"I found some rocks," says Cubby.
"I've got some shells," says Skully.
"Perfect," says Izzy.

"Awesome! You made maracas for the monkey," says Jake. The monkey gives Cubby back his harmonica.

"Thanks!" says Cubby. "Hey, do you wanna come back to Shipwreck Beach and jam with me?"

"Oo-oo-oo," says the happy monkey.

Cubby and the monkey play music together on the beach.

"Blast it, now there's twice as much racket!" says Captain Hook.

"What's the matter?" asks Jake.

"The Cap'n can't have his nappy-nap, what with all that music," says Smee.

"Why didn't you just ask us to be quieter?" asks Jake.

"But, how can I practise for the party?" says Cubby.

"I've got an idea," says Jake.

Cubby and the monkey play a gentle lullaby
for Captain Hook. Mr Smee sings:

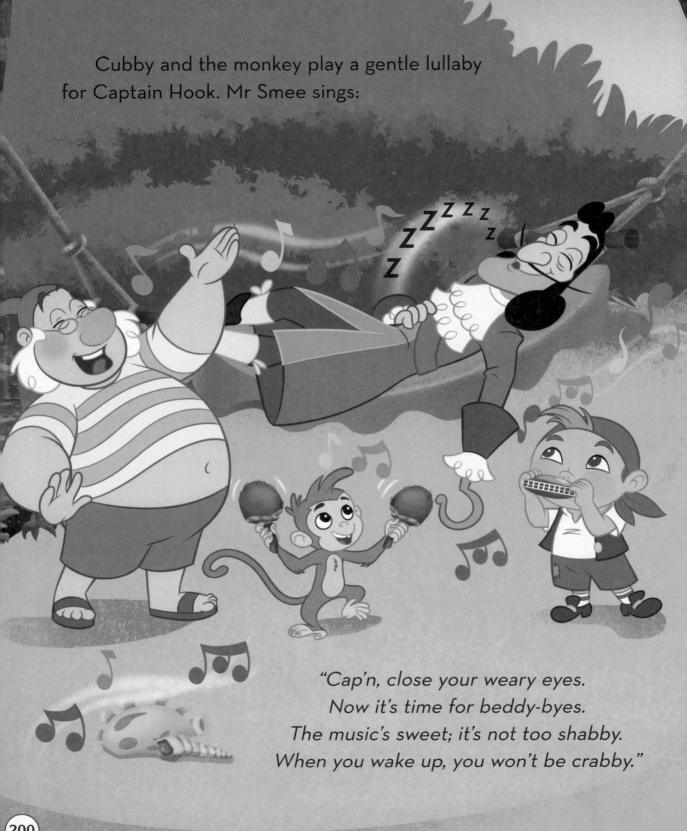

"Cap'n, close your weary eyes.
Now it's time for beddy-byes.
The music's sweet; it's not too shabby.
When you wake up, you won't be crabby."

Hook falls asleep and starts to snore loudly!
"We'd better get ready for the party," says Jake.
"What? I can't hear you over all that noise," says Skully.

Later that night, Cubby and the monkey play their instruments at Marina's party!

"Cubby, thank you so much for playing," says Marina. "You were amazing!"

"You're welcome," says Cubby, blushing.

"Yo-ho, way to go!" says Jake. "See? All that practising paid off!"

"Can't you hear it, Smee?" says Captain Hook.

"Hear what, Cap'n?" asks Smee.

"That blasted lullaby. I can't get it out of me head," says Hook.

"Oh dear, you're imagining things, Cap'n," says Smee.

"I guess I am," says Hook.

"I can see why. It was a very catchy tune, if I do say so myself," says Smee. "And the lyrics were top-notch."

Uh-oh! The monkey has stowed away on the *Jolly Roger*!

205

"If Hook had just asked us to be quiet, we wouldn't have gone through all that trouble today," says Jake.

"Yeah, Hook should know better! If you need something, you should ask nicely," says Izzy.

"Yeah, but if the monkey hadn't taken the harmonica, we never would've got to jam together!" says Cubby.

The End